BEST EVER
Monster
Activities

First published by Parragon in 2013
Parragon
Chartist House
15–17 Trim Street
Bath BA1 1HA, UK
www.parragon.com

Written by Jason Loborik   Illustrated by Steve Wood
Edited by Grace Harvey   Designed by Steve Wood, Kate Merritt, and Claire Brisley
Production by Jack Aylward

ISBN 978-1-4723-1714-8

Printed in China

BEST EVER
Monster
Activities

PaRragon

Bath • New York • Singapore • Hong Kong • Cologne • Delhi
Melbourne • Amsterdam • Johannesburg • Shenzhen

LAKE LURKER!

Give this lake monster some humps!

Can you see five more birds like me? Circle them.

MONSTER MAZE

ENTER IF YOU DARE!

EXIT

Add some monster noises.

Make your monster noises out loud— ROAR!

GRRR!

ROAR!

MONSTER BITE

Finding your way out of a monster maze is tough stuff—monsters jump out at every corner! Are you brave enough to enter?

PICNIC IN THE PARK

This monster has eaten lots of food!
Draw it in her tummy.

Make this sandwich even taller.

How many cupcakes can you count?

9

HAIRY HANDFUL!

How many baby monsters are there?
Color the number.

3 4 5

Color the picture to match
the one on the left.

Draw the
monster's curly
horns.

BEEP BEEP!

Can you spot five differences in the picture below?

Color a monster footprint for each difference you find.

Count the number of sploshy monsters in each color group. Write the numbers in the boxes.

Draw more googly eyes on the monsters!

QUICK! HIDE!

Draw three more trash can monsters.

Aaaargh! There's a big critter in my trash!

SKATEBOARD MONSTERS
Color the monsters and their boards.

WHEEE! This is fun!

Trace over the skateboards so these monsters can join the fun!

MATCH IT!

Draw in the missing footprints to connect each monster to its trail.

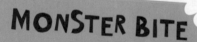

MONSTER BITE

If you ever see great big footprints in the mud, whatever you do, don't follow them—they might have been made by a monster!

How many little slime monsters can you count?

MERRY MONSTERS

Draw smiley faces on these monsters.

How many monsters have feelers on their head like this one?

Give this happy monster
more spikes on his head.

SEA BUDDIES

How many orange fish are there? Color the number.

5 6 7

MONSTERS OF THE NIGHT!

Circle the **biggest** monster.

These little critters have taken over the building!

Find each of these little pictures in the big picture above.

How many monsters are on the roof?

Circle the smallest monster.

MONSTER BITE

Have you ever seen a stone gargoyle on an old building? People used to believe they scared off evil spirits!

VROOM!

Draw wheels on the rest of the trucks so the monsters can finish their race.

MONSTER BITE

Monster trucks have enormous wheels that squash everything in their path!

27

TROLL MONSTER!

Trace over this scary monster. Then color him in!

MONSTER BITE

According to old stories, trolls were nasty monsters who lived in caves. They came out at night to hunt!

Draw your own made-up troll monster hiding in the cave!

Don't make your monster too scary, please!

How many mice can you count?

29

NEXT, PLEASE!

Which monster shape comes next in each row?
Draw its picture.

Only one body part in each box belongs
to this monster. Circle each one.

Now finish the monster
by drawing the missing
body parts.

BOO!

MONSTER DESIGNER

Design your own monsters!
Will they have 1 arm or 10 arms, **2** legs or **8** legs?
Will they be furry or scaly? It's up to you!

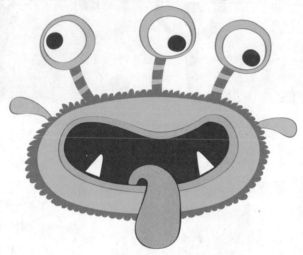

Give each monster a name.

UNDER THE SEA!

Draw your own sea monster here.

Can't catch me!

BOING!

What are these monsters saying?

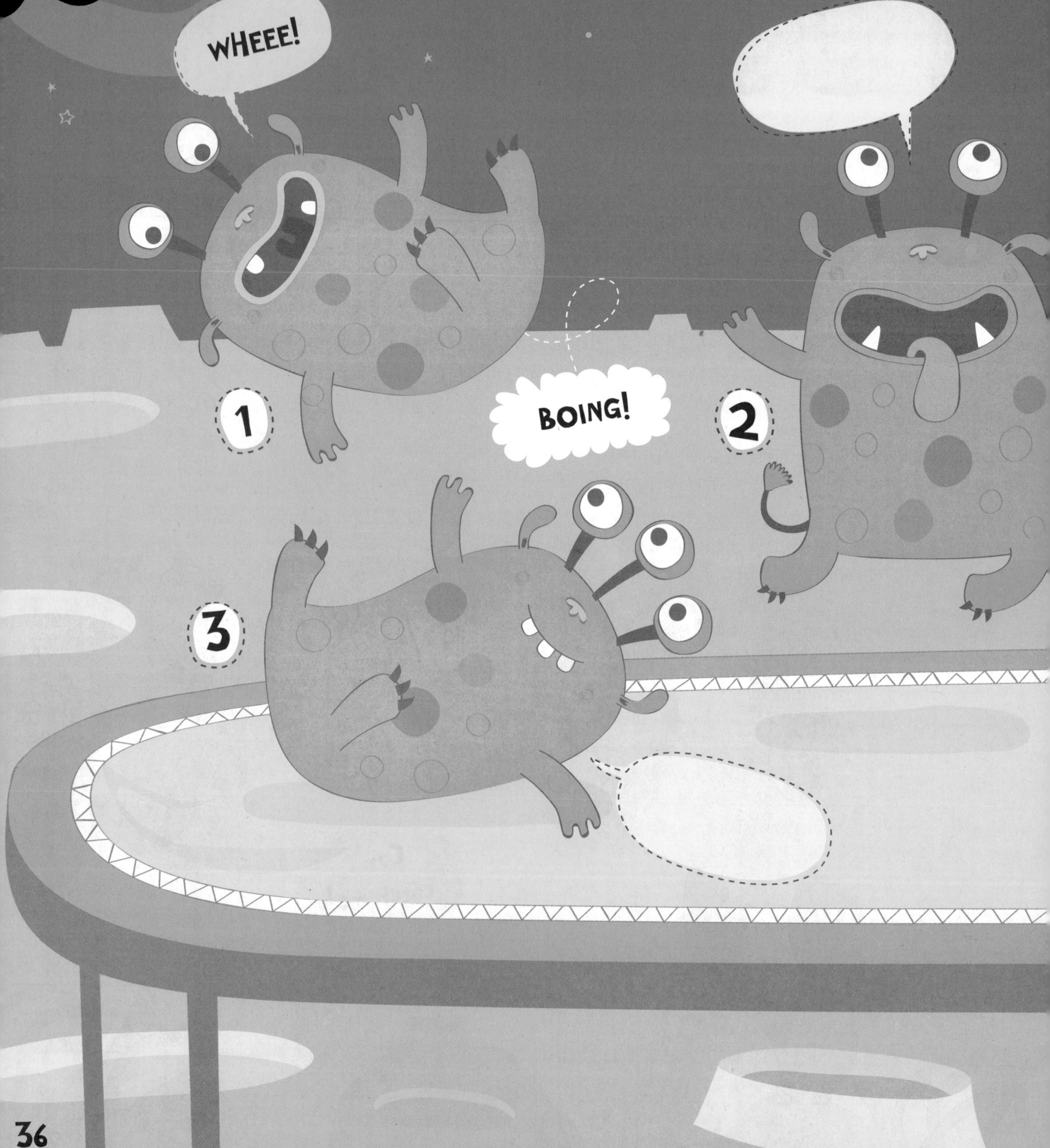

Which two monsters look exactly the same? [ ] and [ ]

LOTS OF LIMBS!

Give this monster eight more tickly tentacles.

Give this monster four arms.

Give this monster five more eyes on stalks.

What do you think this baby monster is dreaming about?
Draw it here:

How many little monsters can you count on the mobile?

BOOGIE WOOGIE!

Draw more raindrops falling down.

I love dancing in the rain!

Trace over the umbrella to keep this monster dry!

MUMMY MONSTERS!

Draw some bandages on the mummy monsters.

MONSTER BITE

Mummy monsters are a little bit like zombies— they don't have brains, so they aren't very smart!

HMMM, YUMMY!

Trace over the lines to see
what the monster is eating.

Here are some more hungry monsters.
Draw some food in each monster's big mouth!

SHADOW MATCH!

Match each monster to its shadow
on the next page.

How many monsters
have spiky bodies?

How many monsters
have spotted bodies?

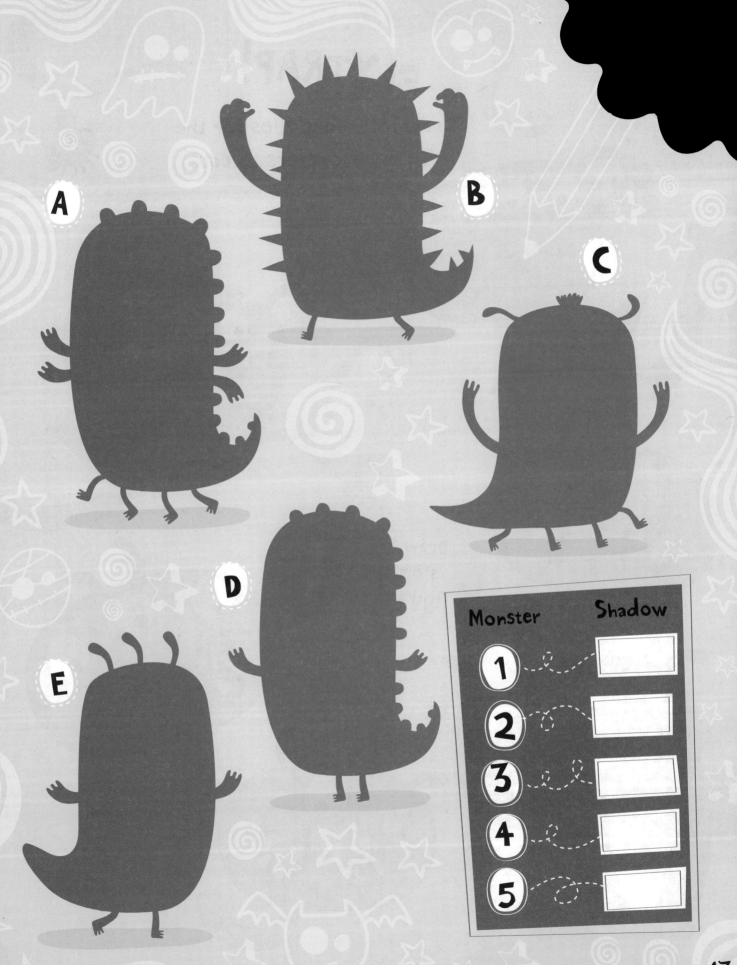

FLYTRAP!

Draw lots more flies for the flytrap monsters to eat.

Draw some more stems on these flytrap monsters.

How many long tongues can you count?

He's completely batty!

How many bats are there?
Color the number.

789

GROSS GROUPS

How many monsters are
there in each group?

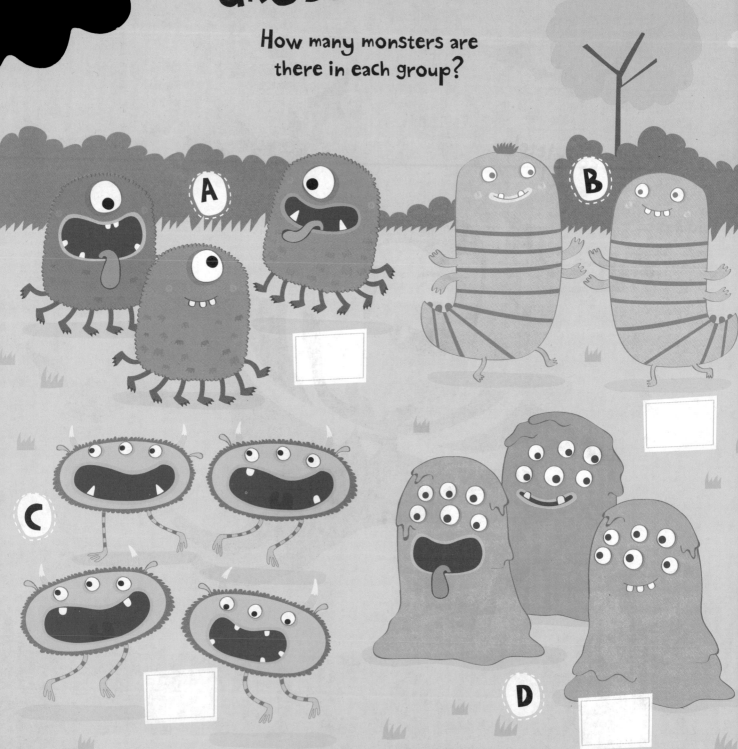

Circle the group with the
most monsters in it!

53

Trace over the castle.

Draw some fire coming out of this monster's mouth.

MONSTER BITE

According to legends, huge fire-breathing lizards called dragons could fly through the air!

55

DRAGON DRAWING

1 Draw an oval body.

2 Add four legs.

3 Now add the head, neck, tail, and spikes.

Add wings so it can fly!

Practice drawing your dragon here.

Now draw your dragon
in this picture, guarding its gold.

57

MONSTER BITE

These lizardlike
monsters protected
their treasure from
would-be thieves!

SLIPPERY SLIME

Color all the slime monsters.

How many monsters are there on this page?

59

RACE IN THE PARK!

Can you spot four differences
in the bottom picture?

60

This monster has four arms!
Color him in!

MONSTER BITE

This monster can brush his fur, brush his teeth, eat his breakfast, and pack his school bag all at the same time!

SPACE MONSTERS!

Trace over the monsters.

Who will you draw looking out of the spaceship?

Fill the night sky with
more stars and planets.

Yoo-hoo!

MONSTER BITE

Believe it or not, a family
of 20 monsters can live
comfortably inside one of
these spaceships. Space
monsters can shrink and grow
whenever they feel like it!

MONSTER MEALS

What is each monster eating?
Follow the squiggly lines to find out.

MONSTER BITE

Monsters are always hungry. They would eat all day and all night long if they could!

1 ----------
2 ----------
3 ----------

What do you think this monster is dreaming about? Draw it in the space.

How many bones can you count?

SILLY CYCLISTS

Draw a racetrack for these monsters,
so that they know which way to go.

Woo-hoo!
I'm doing a
wheelie!

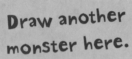

Draw another
monster here.

MONSTER MIX-UP!

Match the top half of each monster
with its bottom half.

That's not my bottom!

1

2

3

4

A

B

C

D

Top half	1	2	3	4
Bottom half				

68

BLOBBY MONSTER

Draw the other half of this blobby monster face.

Give him a name: _____

SCARY SCRIBBLES!

Give this scribble monster some scribbly friends!

Give this monster a tall body.

Scribble a body for this monster.

Draw your own scribble monsters in this space.

Give this monster a wide body.

FEARSOME FOREST!

Color in Frankenstein's monster.

If you color him green, that'll be REALLY scary!

This monster has three big eyes.
Trace over the lines, then color him in!

PEEKABOO!

How many monsters are hiding in the bedroom?

Trace over the closet, then color it in.

MONSTER BITE

Monsters like to hide where you least expect them, so always be on the lookout!

MONSTER ACROBATS

Color the rest of the pennants.

Color the picture.

Hey, stop wobbling around!

Draw mouths on these monsters. Are they happy or sad?

78

Draw your own monster acrobats here!

BUG MONSTER BODY PARTS

This monster has 6 body parts.

Give this monster
5 body parts.

Give this monster
4 body parts.

Give this monster
7 body parts.

How many mummy monsters can you count?

MONSTER MASH!

Add dancing bodies to these floating monster heads!

Help! I have
NO BODY
to dance with!

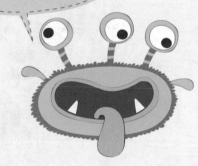

MONSTER BITE

Monsters love dancing.
The dance floor is
always full when you go
to a monster disco!

FLYING HIGH!

Color these monsters red.

Color these monsters orange.

Color these monsters green.

MONSTER BITE

Rainbow monsters live in the clouds. So the next time you think you see a rainbow, take a closer look!

Color these monsters yellow.

Color these monsters blue.

Color these monsters pink.

RED RASCALS, GREEN GREMLINS

Some of these monsters need to be colored in.
Color them in following the outlines.

I'm feeling pale!

How many green monsters are there?

How many red monsters are there?

Connect the dots to find out what's on the monster's head!

5

5

4   6

6   4

7

7   3

3

8

8

2   2

9

9

1   1

87

NIGHTMARE NOISES!

Make up some scary noises for the monsters to make.

BOO!

GRRR!

MONSTER BITE

Beware! Monsters love jumping out in front of you when you least expect them to. Boo!

BEASTLY BUGS

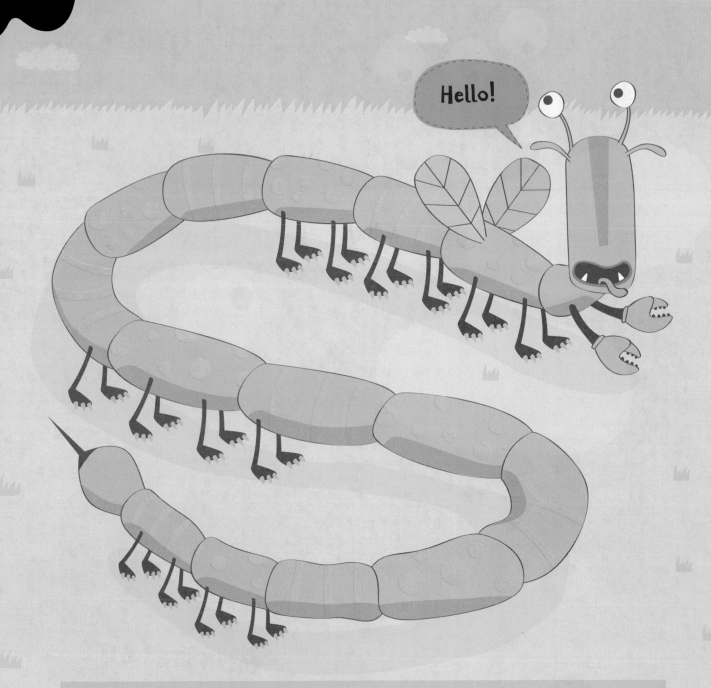

Trace over this bug monster's name.

Bugsy

Color the picture to match the one on the left.

Now give this bug monster a name:

MIX-UP MONSTERS!

Color the monsters.
Use a different color for each one.

Now color this monster, which is a mixture of the monsters on the left. Match the colors of his body parts to those of the monsters.

1

5

3

I'm a mixed-up monster!

4

2

BLOB MONSTERS!

Who has the most eyes?

Doodle your own blob monster here!

Give your blob monster a name:

Trace over the spaceship.

Draw another space monster peeking out of this crater!

MONSTER BITE

Monsters that live on other planets speak different languages. These monsters speak "Monsternese."

BALL PIT FUN!

Can you find five monsters in the ball pit?
Check the boxes as you find them.

Give this monster two more balls to juggle with.

1 2 3 4 5

Draw more balancing balls on this monster's head.

101

RIVER ROWING RACE!

How many oars can you count on this boat?

Who's going to win?

Help this team win by drawing another rower here.

Trace over the trophy. Then color it in!

WHO'S NEXT?

Which monster shape comes next in each row?
Draw its picture.

SLIME TRAIL!

Which one of these trails leads to the slug monster?

ROOAAAR!

This scary monster's roar is so loud,
he's blowing everything away!

106

MONSTER MUNCHIES!

This greedy monster has been eating lots of food.
Draw some more food in his belly!

SCARY SHADOWS

Which shadow matches the fire-breathing dragon?

MONSTERS ON ICE!

Draw different patterns on the scarves.

Give each monster a pom-pom hat.

How many monsters can you count?

113

GRISLY GROOMING

Color this picture.

114

115

PECULIAR PATTERNS

Check your favorite monsters.

Can I be spotted, please?

Draw patterns on these monsters.

Draw the other half of each monster.

Now color them all in!

SLIMY SWIMMING!

Add lots more slime monsters.

Draw eyes on the slime monsters.

I'm having the SLIME of my life!

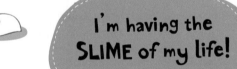

TOXIC SLIME

Draw some more patches of slime on the side of the barrel.

MONSTER BITE

Monsters love living in anything slimy, gooey, or smelly!

MONSTER MUDFIGHT!

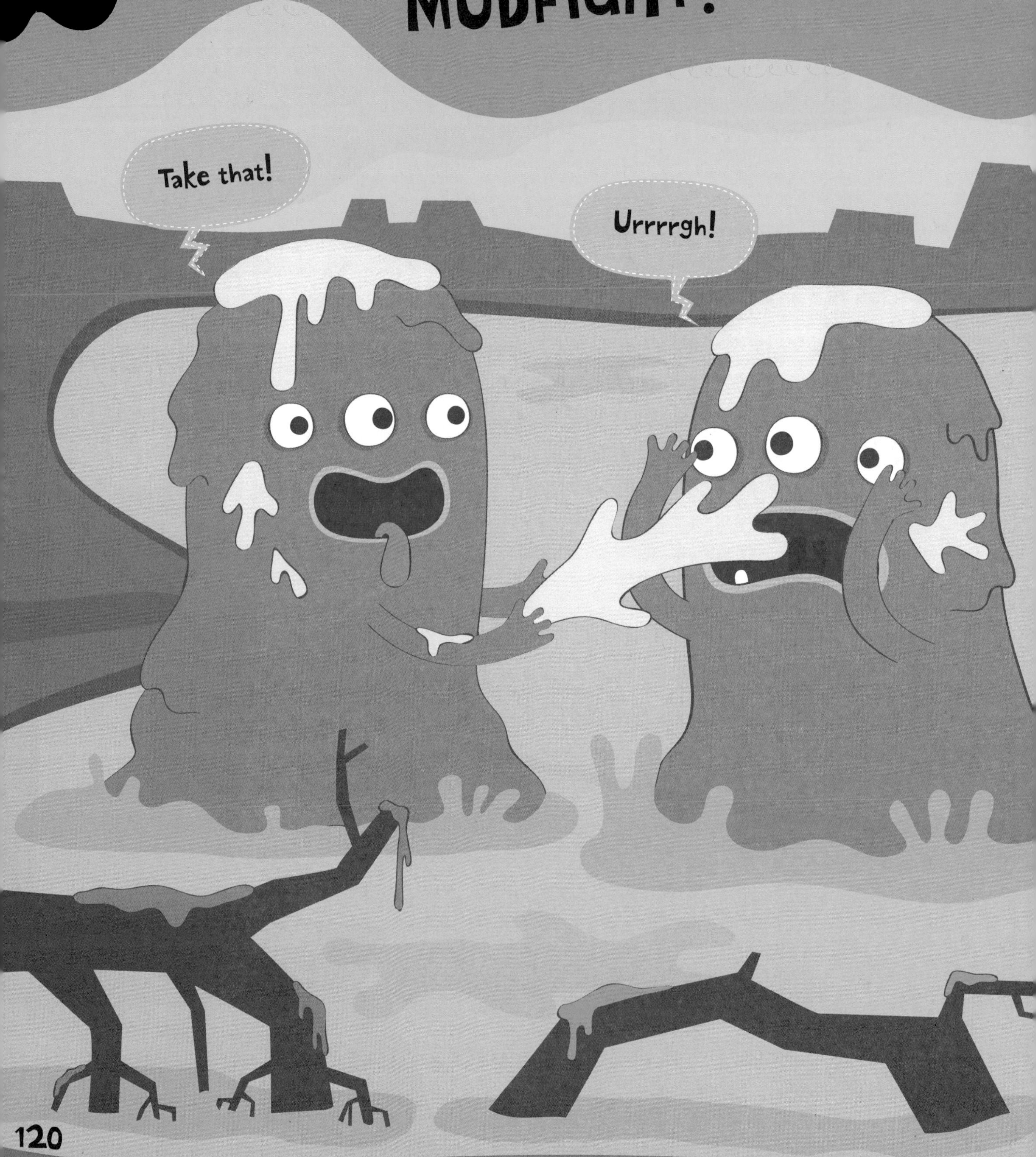

Trace over these mud monsters and color them in.

Color the branches and add more mud.

121

Can you spot four differences
in the bottom picture?

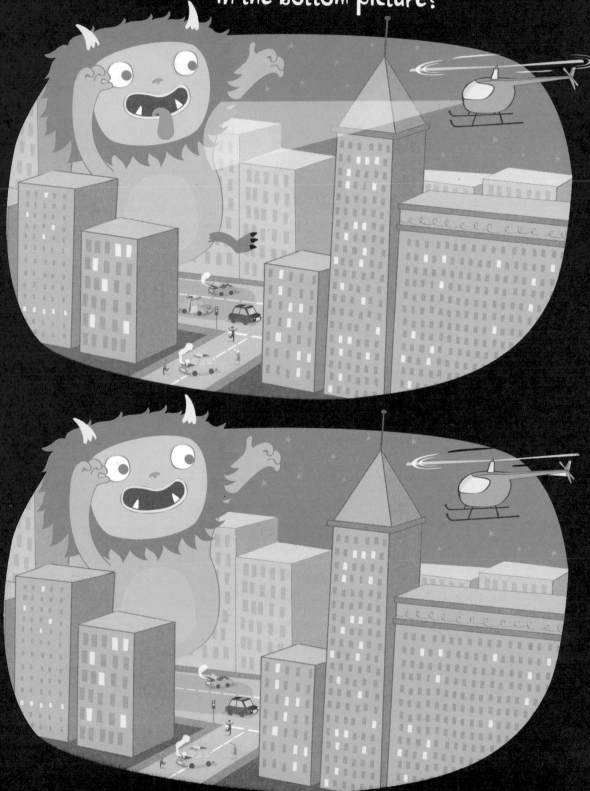

Help the baby monsters get across the swamp to their mommy on the other side!

Mommy, Mommy!

1 2 3 4

Which plank should the baby monsters walk across?

LOUD AND LONG!

Finish these noisy monsters.

BEACH BEASTS

How many monsters are there?
Color the number.

→ **678**

Help!
I'm stuck!

Which monster
has the most eyes?

E

Give this monster three eyestalks.

MONSTER BITE

Monster mischief is more tiring than you think. That's why monsters go on vacation, too—to take a break from scaring people!

F

G

Draw another monster in the deck chair.

ONE FOR ME, ONE FOR YOU!

Draw lines to divide the cake into four equal pieces.

Draw party hats on the rest of the monsters.

I want cake!

Me too!

ODD MONSTER OUT

Draw a circle around the odd one out in each group.

HORRIFYING HALVES

Draw the other half of each monster.

I'm not half the monster I used to be.

131

SNOWY SLEDDING

Color each monster's hat the same color as its scarf.

133

ZOOOOOM!

Circle the smallest monster in each group.

How many monsters can you count altogether?

Give the machine flashing lights.

Draw loops to connect the rest of the wires with those on the monster's helmet.

MONSTER BITE

A mad scientist named Doctor Frankenstein invented his very own monster and brought it to life with electricity!

Draw another Bigfoot monster.

3

MONSTER BITE

These hairy creatures might live in the forests and look like apes, but don't be fooled, these are Bigfoot monsters!

FASHIONABLE FURRIES!

Draw more spots on this hat.

Draw more stripes on this hat.

Draw a line from each square to the matching monster in the picture.

BOO!
Connect the dots to find out who's trying to scare you!

Tee-hee, scared you!

142

I'm just a nose-body!

Turn this big eye into a monster by giving it arms and legs!

Add some eyes, legs, and arms to turn these body parts into monsters.

144

145

MONSTER MATCH

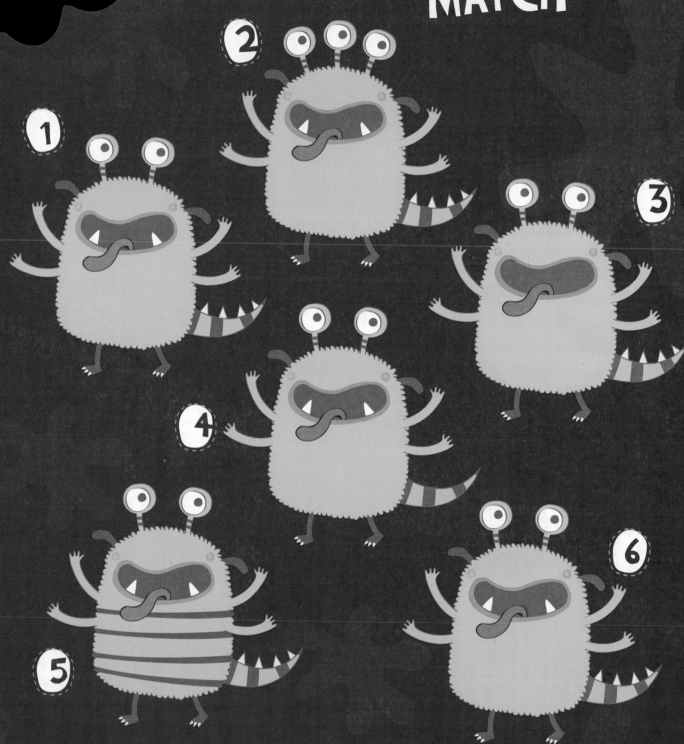

Which two monsters look exactly the same? [   ] and [   ]

Give these monsters some brothers and sisters!

Draw another monster that's bigger than these two.

Draw another monster that's smaller than these two.

Draw another monster the same size as these two.

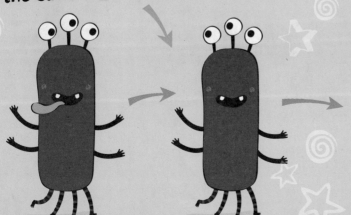

MONSTER INVADERS!

Draw some spaceships for these flying monsters.

Give each monster more tentacles.

How many monsters can you count?

MONSTER BITE

Monster spaceships can beam you up into the air!

149

CLICK! SNAP!

These monsters have been traveling far and wide!
Color in the famous places they have visited.

If you like a photo, color the star next to it!

The Statue of Liberty in New York.

The Eiffel Tower in Paris, France.

The Sydney Opera House in Sydney, Australia.

The Taj Mahal in Uttar Pradesh, India.

Big Ben in London, England.

ZANY ZOMBIES

Draw in the other half of each zombie.

MONSTER BITE

These zombie monsters like stomping around and chasing people. Scary!

Color all the monsters.

How many monsters are round?

How many monsters are triangular?

How many monsters are square?

THUMB THINGS!

These funny monsters are made from thumbprints.

Add more eyes, arms, and legs wherever you like!

155

HELTER SKELTER!

How many monsters are there on this page? Color the number.

4 5 6

SUN AND SAND!

Can you spot five differences
in the picture below?

Color a beach ball for each difference you find.

158

What is each monster eating?
Follow the squiggly lines to find out.

I want to eat everything!

What is each monster eating?

1 _____

2 _____

3 _____

MONSTER BITE

Monsters aren't fussy eaters. They'll eat dirty socks, mud pies, and moldy cheese.

159

INTO THE DEEP!

Trace over the lines to find out what's in the sea!

Draw some more sea monsters!

Hope I'm not their lunch!

Give these sea
monsters lots
more tentacles.

MONSTER BITE

Giant squid monsters
can tip over ships with
their big long tentacles!

161

MONSTER BAKES!

Draw some more cake mix slopping everywhere!

Decorate these cupcakes however you like.

How many cupcakes
can you count?

MONSTER BITE

Have you noticed how monsters
always like making a mess?

WHO'S IN LINE?

Which monster comes next in each row?
Draw its picture.

Now draw some more monsters in the spaces.
Make sure the total number in each group is five.

TICKLE MONSTER!

Draw lots more arms and hands on this monster.

I'm such a handy monster to have around!

Draw your own monster in this space.
Will you give it lots of arms or
lots of legs? It's up to you!

MONSTER MAYHEM

These monsters have emptied their toybox!
Which toy is your favorite?

How many balls can you count?

BOING!

PARTY!

Color the monsters' birthday presents.

HAPPY BIRTHDAY TO

Whose birthday is it? Write the monster's name here!

170

Surprise!

Draw a monster jumping out of the box.

How many presents can you count altogether?

TERRIFYING TEETH

Draw some monster faces to
go with each set of teeth.

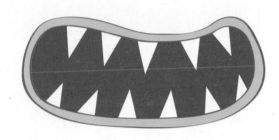

Rarrrrgh!

Grrr!

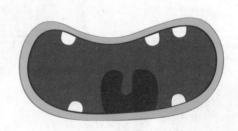

Draw as many big teeth as you can to fill this monster's mouth!

YETI MONSTER!

1 Draw an oval body and two legs.

2 Add the Yeti's head and two big paws.

3 Now go over the lines to give your Yeti a shaggy body!

Make sure your Yeti has a friendly face.

MONSTER BITE

Yetis are also called Abominable Snowmen!

Draw your very own Yeti here!

Make sure it's a scary Yeti!

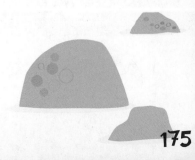

MONSTER FAMILIES

Draw a line to connect each
monster mommy to her baby.

Have you seen
my mommy?

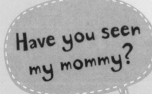

How many legs does each sausage monster have? Write it in the circles.

Draw your own sausage monster in this space.

HIDE-AND-SEEK!

How many trees can you count?

Do you think anyone's found us?

Not YET-i!

Draw footprints leading up to these Yeti.

Draw two more Yeti monsters peeking out!

MONSTER BITE

Yetis live in snowy
mountains because they
love having snowball fights!

SCARY SLEEPERS

Draw two more teddy bears.

Color the rest of the blanket.

What is this monster dreaming about?
Draw it in the space.

How many monsters are there?
Color the number.

HAIRY AND HUNGRY!

Help the monster through the maze
to the big apple pie at the other end!

Draw the monster eating his apple pie.

Trace over some more food for the monster to eat.
Then color it in!

Am I the smallest?

1 2 3 4

Put the monsters in order.

Which monster is the smallest?

Which monster has the most eyes?

Which monster has the most feet?

SHOCKING SEAS!

Can you spot four differences in the picture below?

Color a fish for each difference you find.

These sea monsters are mixed up.
Draw a line to match each top half
to the right bottom half.

Hold on. I've got flippers, not tentacles!

ANSWERS

Pages 4–5

Page 6

Pages 8–9
There are 17 cupcakes.

Page 10
There are 5 baby monsters.

Page 12

Page 13
There are 5 blue monsters.
There are 3 green monsters.
There are 4 red monsters.
There are 2 purple monsters.

Pages 18–19
There are 6 little slime monsters.

Page 20
There are 2 monsters with feelers on their head.

Pages 22–23
There are 5 orange fish.

Pages 24–25
There are 4 monsters on the roof.

Pages 28–29
There are 5 mice.

Pages 30–31

Pages 34–35
There are 6 jellyfish.

Pages 36–37
Monsters 1 and 4 look exactly the same.

Page 39
There are 10 little monsters on the mobile.

ANSWERS

Pages 46–47
1E, 2A, 3B, 4C, 5D
1 monster has a spiky body.
2 monsters have spotted bodies.

Pages 48–49
There are 6 long tongues.

Pages 50–51
There are 9 bats.

Page 52
There are 3 monsters in A.
There are 2 monsters in B.
There are 4 monsters in C.
There are 3 monsters in D.

Page 53
D is the tallest.
A is the shortest.
B has the most eyes.
C has the fewest legs.

Pages 58–59
There are 4 monsters on this page.

Page 60

Page 64
1 is eating the plate of worms.
2 is eating the cake.
3 is eating the bowl of food.

Page 65
There are 7 bones.

Pages 66–67
7 has the most teeth.

Page 68
1C, 2D, 3B, 4A

Pages 74–75
There are 8 monsters hiding in the bedroom.

Pages 76–77

Page 81
There are 11 mummy monsters.

Page 86
There are 4 green monsters.
There are 5 red monsters.

Page 87

Page 94
A has the most eyes.

ANSWERS

Page 96

Pages 98–99
There are 7 little green monsters.

Pages 100–101

Page 102
There are 6 oars on the blue boat.

Page 104

Page 105
Trail 3 leads to the slug monster.

Page 110
3 matches the fire monster exactly.

Pages 112–113
There are 8 monsters.

Page 122

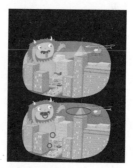

Page 123
The baby monsters should walk across plank 1.

Pages 126–127
There are 7 monsters.
G has the most eyes.

Page 129

Pages 134–135
There are 12 monsters altogether.

ANSWERS

Pages 140–141
There are 9 monsters.

Page 142

Page 146
Monsters 1 and 6 look exactly the same.

Pages 148–149
There are 5 monsters.

Page 153
6 monsters are round.
5 monsters are triangular.
4 monsters are square.

Page 156
There are 6 monsters on this page.

Page 158

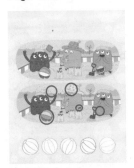

Page 159
1 is eating the apple.
2 is eating the ice cream.
3 is eating the hamburger.

Pages 162–163
There are 7 cupcakes.

Page 164

Pages 165

ANSWERS

Pages 168–169
There are 8 balls.

Pages 170–171
There are 11 presents altogether.

Page 176

Page 177
The blue monster has 8 legs.
The red monster has 10 legs.
The yellow monster has 6 legs.

Pages 178–179
There are 13 trees.

Pages 180–181
There are 7 monsters.

Page 182

Page 184
There are 8 monsters.

Page 185
Smallest to tallest: **3, 2, 4, 1**
Most to least number of eyes: **2, 1, 4, 3**
Most to least number of feet and tentacles: **3, 2, 4, 1**

Page 186

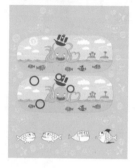

Page 187